Alfie sat down. He felt sad. 'The elephants will come back for me,' he said to himself. 'I will wait here.'

Alfie waited by the bushes. Then he saw some animals coming towards him. They were zebras.

2

'Have you seen the elephants?' asked Alfie. 'They have gone away. I am all by myself.'

The zebras had not seen the elephants. 'You can come with us,' they said. 'We will help you find them.'

4

So Alfie left the bushes. He went with the zebras across the grassy land of Africa looking for the elephants.

Suddenly there was a loud roaring noise. ROAR!

A lion was near. The zebras set off running fast.

6

The zebras ran this way and that way. They ran round and round. Alfie was stuck in the middle.

Soon all the zebras had gone. The lion had gone. Alfie was all by himself in the middle of Africa.